VENGEANCE OF
VAMPIRELLA

RETURN OF THE BLOOD RED QUEEN

ART THIS PAGE BY TOMMY CASTILLO AND MIKE KELLEHER

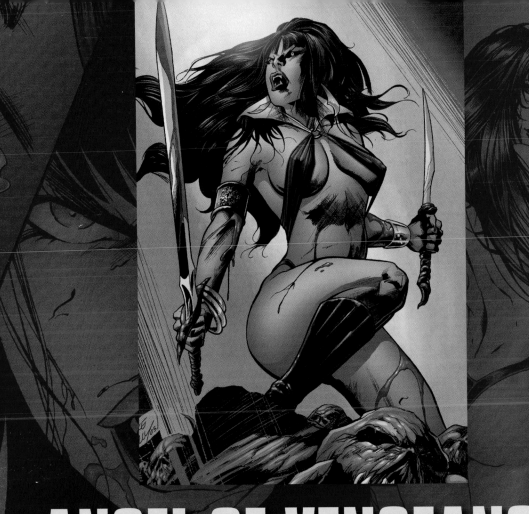

ANGEL OF VENGEANCE

VAMPIRELLA'S ENTIRE LIFE WAS A LIE.
In one terrible moment,
she learned the truth and lost her way.

Now she seeks a new direction, a new purpose.
The desire to do good is all she has left, but now even that is
consumed with anger and emptiness.

Into this void, a new purpose comes:
A QUEST FOR VENGEANCE
driven by an unknown force...

For more, read *Vampirella Revelations TPB*.

YOU WANT TO KNOW HOW I WOUND UP HERE?

IT WASN'T JEALOUSY, OR GAMBLING, OR DOPE, OR GREED.

NONE OF THE STUFF THAT LANDS MOST GUYS HERE.

IT WAS A BRUNETTE.

A BRUNETTE SENT ME TO HELL.

INK

ORY: PHIL HESTER · ART: STEPHEN SEGOVIA · COLORS: JAY DAVID RAMOS

TTERING: ED DUKESHIRE · SPECIAL THANKS: GLASS HOUSE GRAPHICS · MASTER: BON ALIMAGNO

NOT AGAIN, MAN. YOU DON'T GET SICK OF TELLING THAT STORY?

GO AHEAD, BUDDY, TELL IT AGAIN. I LIKE HEARING IT.

PASSES THE TIME.

A REAL NICE PLACE, YOU KNOW? UPSCALE. NOT ONE OF THOSE BACK ALLEY HEPATITIS FARMS. WE WERE RIGHT BY THE BIG CASINOS, EVEN HAD A RECEPTIONIST.

AND A CLASSY CLIENTELE, TOO. PORN STARS, ATHLETES, HIGH ROLLERS. YOU KNOW I WORKED ON RODMAN, RIGHT?

NO KIDDING?

YEAH. HELL, I EVEN PUT A BUTTERFLY ON GWEN STEFANI'S ASS. GWEN STEFANI, MAN!

IT WAS BACK WHEN I HAD MY TATTOO SHOP IN VEGAS, I TOLD YOU GUYS ABOUT MY SHOP, RIGHT?

YEAH, YOU TOLD US.

ANYWAY, I WAS WORKING LATE ONE NIGHT, JUST ABOUT READY TO PACK IT IN, WHEN THIS BABE WALKS IN LIKE YOU WOULDN'T BELIEVE.

HOT?

BEYOND HOT. THE KIND YOU MARRY FOR THE PRIVILEGE OF DRINKING HER BATH WATER.

TOO SHORT TO BE A SHOWGIRL AND TOO FINE TO BE A STRIPPER.

BUT EVEN THROUGH HER COAT I COULD SEE SHE HAD A BODY ANY CHICK ON THE STRIP WOULD KILL FOR.

SORRY, LADY. WE'RE CLOSING.

CLOSING? I THOUGHT THIS WAS A TWENTY-FOUR HOUR TOWN.

YEAH, WELL, I'M NOT A TWENTY-FOUR HOUR GUY.

SHE ROLLED ON HER STOMACH AND HER GLOSSY ANIMAL BLACK HAIR PARTED, REVEALING A FLAWLESS ALABASTER BACK.

MY CANVAS, THAT'S WHAT SHE SAID.

MY MASTERPIECE.

I WAS DEAD ON MY FEET, BURNT OUT FROM A HARD DAY'S WORK, BUT SOMETHING CAME OVER ME.

I WAS GOOD, THE BEST IN LAS VEGAS, BUT THE WORK I DID ON THAT LADY'S SKIN WAS SO FAR OVER MY HEAD I COULDN'T EVEN PICTURE IT IN A DREAM.

I DIDN'T TRACE IT OUT, DIDN'T WORK FROM A TEMPLATE. HELL, I THINK I MIGHT HAVE DONE SOME OF IT WITH MY EYES CLOSED.

THE NEEDLES WERE FLYING ON THEIR OWN THAT NIGHT, BUZZING LIKE LITTLE HUMMING BIRDS WHILE I SQUEEZED THEIR FEVERED LIFE'S BLOOD INTO THE COLORS IN HER FLESH.

E HADN'T BEEN A
N HELL IN MEMORY.

YOU SEE, DEMONS
AREN'T BORN
THESE DAYS, TOM.

THEY'RE MADE.
BY INIQUITY, BY
WICKEDNESS.

LIKE A CANCER, EVIL
EATS MEN FROM THE
INSIDE, HOLLOWING
THEM OUT AND WEARING
THEIR SKIN LIKE COATS.

THAT BABY GREW TO KILL
MANY OF THEIR KIND.

VAMPIRES. GHOULS.
BEASTS OF ALL
SORTS LOOSED
UPON THE WORLD.

THAT'S SOME STORY.

HERE'S THE IMPORTANT PART FOR YOU, TOM.

THAT BABY SLEW SO MANY DEMONS THAT SHE EVEN HAD TIME TO TURN HER ATTENTIO TO THOSE WHO HA NOT YET BECOME SLAVES OF HELL, BL WERE DEMONS IN THE MAKING.

SHE ABORTED THEM, AS IT WERE.

I HAD FRAMED HER BACK IN ORNATE IVY AND ARCANE PATTERNS, LEAVING A CLEAR SPACE FOR THE FEATURED IMAGE.

SHE WANTED TO BE MY MASTERPIECE, AND I WANTED TO OBLIGE HER. I WANTED TO GIVE HER AN IMAGE SHE'D NEVER FORGET.

THE DEMON KILLER CAME ACROSS THE DYING VICTIM OF ONE SUCH NASCENT DEVIL MANY YEARS AGO.

SHE TOOK TH DYING WOMAN BLOOD IN HE MOUTH SO SH COULD KNOW T CIRCUMSTANC OF THE CRIM

I WANTED TO PUT MYSELF ON THAT BACK. MY FACE, MAYBE THE TWO OF US IN BED.

I WANTED TO BE A PART OF HER FOREVER.

BUT WHEN I BEGAN TO TATTOO HER SKIN THE BLOOD WELLED AROUND THE NEEDLE MORE THAN USUAL.

JUST A LITTLE AT FIRST, ENOUGH THAT I HAD TO WIPE IT AWAY WITH THE STERILE PAD EVERY FEW SECONDS.

THE WOMAN I FOUND HAD BEEN CRUCIFIED. TRUSSED UP ON HOOKS AND CHAINS.

THAT DEMON KILLER IS ME, TOM, AND THAT BLOOD BROUGHT ME TO YOU.

NOW THE BLOOD WAS COMING SO FAST I HAD TO DROP THE NEEDLE AND WIPE WITH BOTH HANDS.

AS FAST AS I BLOTTED, DROPLETS GREW FAT IN THE NEEDLE HOLES AND OVERFLOWED AGAIN.

IT'S ALMOST LIKE SUNDAY SCHOOL IN HERE, ISN'T IT? MY STORY STARTS WITH A NATIVITY AND ENDS WITH A CRUCIFIXION.

ART BY JOE JUSKO

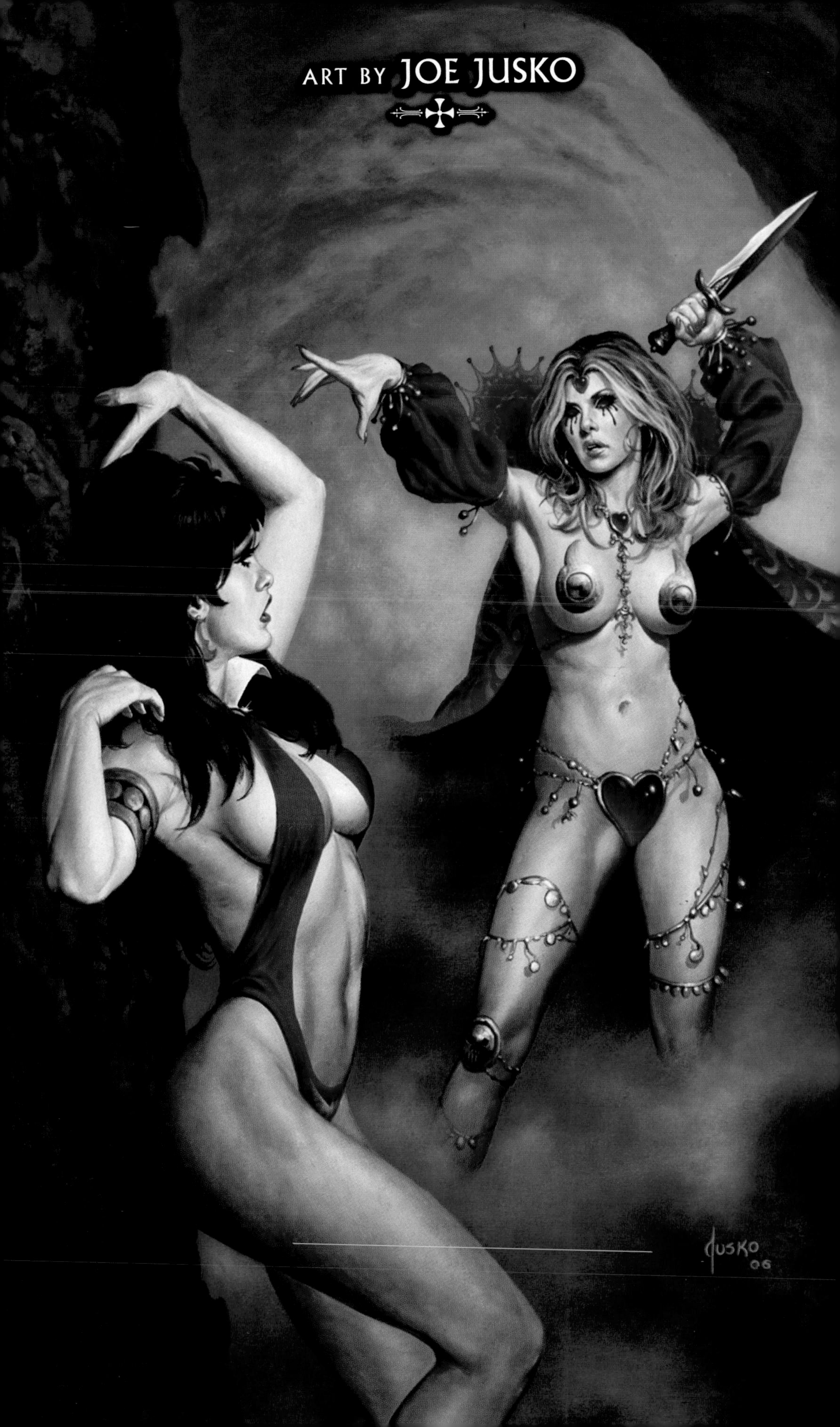

ONE, PLEASE.

WE ALL THINK WE'RE THE MASTERS OF OUR OWN DESTINIES.

FIGURING THAT THE COINCIDENCES ARE JUST THAT...

NOW SHOWING

NOW SHOWING

ONE PLEASE...

NO CHARGE.

SURE, IT FEELS LIKE FATE CAN BE TWISTING THE KNIFE SOMETIMES.

BUT, NINE TIMES OUT OF TEN, IT'S OUR OWN HAND THAT'S PUSHING ON THE TANG OF THE BLADE... SHOVING THE CUTTING EDGE EVER DEEPER.

TRUTH BE TOLD...
THERE'S NOBODY
PLOTTING
AGAINST YOU.

NO ONE KNOWS
YOUR EVERY
MOVE.

AND WHEN YOU'RE
ALL ALONE...
NO ONE THERE
TO STOP YOU...

YOU'LL FIND YOU'RE
CAPABLE OF THE
DAMNDEST THINGS.

Vengeance of Vampirella

PART 1 OF 3

JOSHUA HALE FIALKOV
WRITER

STEPHEN SEGOVIA
ARTIST

JAY DAVID RAMOS
COLORIST

ED DUKESHIRE
LETTERER

SPECIAL THANKS:
GLASS HOUSE GRAPHICS

BON ALIMAGNO
EDITOR

PLEASE, DON'T FORCE MY HAND... I BEG YOU...

ART BY STEPHEN SEGOVIA
COLORS BY JAY DAVID RAMOS

"YOU NEVER KNOW WHAT YOU'RE CAPABLE OF 'TIL YOU'RE UP AGAINST A WALL."

PEN WAS ALWAYS FULL OF 'WISDOM' LIKE THAT.

WELL, THE BLOOD RED QUEEN AND THE MAD GOD CHAOS HAVE ME DAMN NEAR CRUCIFIED ON THE WALL...

BUT YOU KNOW WHAT?

Vengeance of Vampirella

JOSHUA HALE FIALKOV
WRITER

STEPHEN SEGOVIA
ARTIST

JAY DAVID RAMOS
COLORIST

ED DUKESHIRE
LETTERER

SPECIAL THANKS:
GLASS HOUSE GRAPHICS

BON ALIMAGNO
EDITOR

COME NOW, VAMPI, DARLING. YOU KNOW THAT THESE MEN ARE MERELY HIRED HANDS... THE REAL JUICY SOULS ARE THE ONES IN CHARGE.

THESE DON'T EVEN COUNT!

OVER THE PAST FEW DAYS, I'VE BEEN 'RECRUITED' BY THE BLOOD RED QUEEN IN HER INSANE QUEST TO RAISE HER BELOVED, THE MAD GOD CHAOS.

I'VE BEEN COLLECTING SOULS. THE TALLY IS NINE.

EACH DESERVED TO DIE...

CHILD MOLESTORS...

MURDERERS...

JUST PURE EVIL.

I GAVE EACH OF THEM A CHANCE TO REPENT.

THEY COULD'VE SAVED THEIR LIVES... SAVED THEIR SOULS...

LOVE MAKES US DO SOME STRANGE THINGS.

FOOLISH MAN.

SO BE IT, VAMPIRELLA.

I WANTED MORE THAN ANYTHING FOR YOU TO SHARE IN THE REBIRTH OF THE MAD GOD.

YOU OBVIOUSLY COULDN'T BE BOTHERED TO SAVE THE MAN YOU LOVE IN THE PROCESS.

OH... OH DARLING. LOOK WHAT YOU DID NOW.

WHAT ARE YOU...

JUST A LITTLE BIT LONGER... DEAR.

NO, I DIDN'T MEAN--

TEN SOULS, VAMPIRELLA... A PERFECT SET.

HOW CAN THIS...

THE BLADE IS THE CONDUIT, MY LOVE. JUST AS YOUR CRIMES WILL BE THE CONDUIT FOR MY BELOVED...

ART BY NICOLA SCOTT
INKED BY JOE RUBINSTEIN
COLORS BY WES DZIOBA

ART BY LAN MEDINA
INKED BY JOE RUBINSTEIN
COLORS BY WES DZIOBA

VERY EARLY ON, ADAM SHOWED ME SOMETHING...

SOMETHING UNIQUE TO HUMANS.

IF IT'S FOR THE PEOPLE YOU LOVE.

Vengeance of Vampirella

PART 4

Joshua Hale Fialkov
WRITER

Noah Salonga
ARTIST

Jay David Ramos
COLORIST

Ed Dukeshire
LETTERER

SPECIAL THANKS:
Glass House Graphics

Bon Alimagno
EDITOR

TAKE, FOR EXAMPLE...

MORDECAI PENDRAGON.

DRUNK.

SCREW UP.

COOL...
PEN!

I'M GOING TO NEED A LITTLE MORE JUICE.

WE'RE TRYING.

AND SO...
WE DO
WHAT WE
MUST.

TO PROTECT
THE ONES
WE LOVE...

WE SACRIFICE...
GOD, HOW WE
SACRIFICE.

BUT WE GO
ON BECAUSE
WE LOVE.

I FEEL LIKE A BROKEN RECORD.

BLURTING OUT ALL THESE FAUX-PROFOUNDITIES.

THE FACT OF THE MATTER IS, I'D D ANYTHING TO HAV MY ADAM BACK.

EVEN WALK RIC UP TO THE DE HIMSELF, AND K HIM IN THE TEE

ART BY TOM FLEMING

ART BY BILL SIENKIEWICZ

ART BY DAN BRERETON

VAMPIRELLA REVEALED!

et ready to go
ehind the scenes
f the most talked-about
ampirella storyarc
n ages with not one,
ut TWO scripts!

irst is the unique script for the
Vengeance of Vampirella" prelude
nk" by Eisner Award–nominated
riter Phil Hester, author of modern
asterpieces *Deep Sleeper* and
he Coffin. Hester's unique method
reaks up his scripts into two parts
– a document with his dialogue and
age-by-page layouts complete with
umbnails. An artist himself, most
ecently on *The Irredeemable Ant-
Man*, Hester has a masterful grasp of
omics storytelling. You can clearly
ee it in action as he takes advantage
f the medium's possibilities in his
ayouts. Artist Stephen Segovia greatly
ppreciated Hester's method as it
aved him time laying out such a
hallenging story, a process which can
ake longer to do than the drawing of
he pages themselves!

Next is the full script of "Vengeance
f Vampirella, Part 3" by Harvey
ward–nominated writer Joshua
ale Fialkov, author of the highly
cclaimed *Elk's Run*. Fialkov works
ore conventionally, in full script. As
he storyline progressed, Fialkov made
is descriptions less detailed, trusting
egovia's abilities and imagination
 bring his scenes to life in his own
nique way. This particular story
as a high watermark in Vampirella's
istory and Fialkov shares his
houghts on how the script translated
 his commentary.

Notes:

SPLASH PAGE. NICE SHOT OF VAMPI STROLLING DOWN THE VEGAS STRIP AT NIGHT. SHE'S DRESSED IN A FEMININE OVERCOAT, BUT STILL TURNS THE HEADS OF ONLOOKERS IN THE BACKGROUND. HAVE FUN WITH NEON CASINO SIGNS, ETC.

BOTTOM 1/3 OF PAGE OR SO IS ORNATE TITLE RENDERED IN TYPICAL TATTOO IMAGERY - GO NUTS. UP TO YOU & BON IF YOU, THE PENCILER, OR THE LETTERER TACKLES THIS BIT.

CALL ME WITH ANY QUESTIONS.
FEEL FREE TO DEVIATE FROM LAYOUT AS LONG AS BALLOON PLACEMENTS STILL MATCH UP.

Notes:

① - VERTICAL PANEL. LONGSHOT OF VAMPI STROLLING UP TO TOM'S TATTOO SHOP, EMPHASIS ON HIS GAUDY SIGN.

② - INSIDE THE SHOP. ESTABLISHING SHOT. PLENTY OF PIERCING/SUSPENSION GEAR IN FOREGROUND. IN MIDDLE WE SEE TOM TATTOOING MANNY'S HUGE BICEP - YOU CHOOSE THE IMAGE, BUT IT SHOULD BE CLEAR IT'S ONLY ½ DONE. TATTOO SAMPLES ON THE WALL.

③ - VAMPI'S HAND PUSHES OPEN DOOR IN F.G. - TOM & MANNY LOOK UP IN B.G.

④ - CLOSER REACTION SHOT OF TOM & MANNY, STUNNED BY VAMPI'S UBER HOTNESS.

⑤ - OVER THE SHOULDER SHOT PAST TOM TO BACKLIT, SHADOWY VAMPI LOOKING LIKE SHE JUST STEPPED OUT OF A SIN CITY COMIC.

Notes:

① - C.U. SHOT OF VAMPIRELLA FLASHING HER MOST SEDUCTIVE LOOK RIGHT AT US.

② - CLOSE UPSHOT OF HYPNOTIZED TOM - HE LOOKS EQUAL PARTS SCARED & LOVESTRUCK.

③ - FLOATING FIGURES, NO BACKGROUND. VAMPI LOOKS AT MANNY CALMLY, HANDS IN POCKETS.

④ - FRIGHTENED MANNY BOLTS OUT OF HIS CHAIR. SATISFIED VAMPI WATCHES HIM RUN. TOM IS DUMBSTRUCK.

⑤ - LONG DOWNSHOT OF MANNY RUNNING OUT INTO THE STREET IN FRONT OF THE SHOP.

Notes:

① - TOM WATCHES MANNY RUN AWAY FROM GLASS FRONT DOOR. HE'S HOLDING THE "OPEN" SIGN.

② - SAME SHOT, BUT NOW HE HAS A LECHEROUS GRIN AS HE FLIPS OVER "CLOSED" SIGN AND TURNS TO VAMPI.

③ - SILHOUETTE OF VAMPI IN F.G. TOM LOOKS AT HER FROM OVER HIS SHOULDER.

④ - SPLASHY FROM BEHIND TOM. FULL BODY SHOT OF VAMPI TOSSING THE COAT BEHIND HER - SHE IS SUPER SEDUCTIVE.

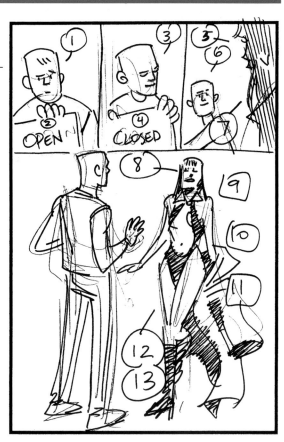

Title: Vampirella- INK **Issue: Halloween Special** **Page:** 5

Notes:

① - C.U. TOM TRYING TO LOOK COOL.

② - FROM BEHIND VAMPI IN FG AS HER BIKINI-THING SLITHERS OFF LIKE SPIDEY'S VENOM COSTUME. TOM IS ASTOUNDED.

③ - C.U. SEDUCTIVE VAMPI - MIRROR OF PAN. 1

④ - SHOT IN SILHOUETTE. VAMPI STRIDES UP TO TOM. THEY ARE FRAMED BY CHAINS, SUSPENSION GEAR.

⑤ OTS PAST TOM DOWN TO SINCERE, ALMOST PLEADING VAMPIRELLA.

Title: Vampirella- INK **Issue: Halloween Special** **Page:** 6

Notes:

① - VAMPI RESTS ON HER STOMACH ON A MASSAGE TABLE, HER NUDITY OBSCURED BY TOM'S FIGURE IN F.G MAY WANT TO MOVE CAMERA OUT SO TOM'S HEAD FITS IN SHOT - YOU CHOOSE.

② - C.U. TOM CONSUMED BY DESIRE, SWEATING LIKE A JUNKIE.

③ - PERSPECTIVE SHOT, TOM FEVERISHLY TATTOOING VAMPI'S BACK. SHE HAS A TOWEL OVER HER PERFECT BEHIND.

Notes:

① - SHOT PAST VAMPI IN F.G. TO BUSY TOM.

② - DOWNSHOT OF SCENE - REMEMBER TOWEL OVER VAMPI'S ASS.

③ - M.C.U. PROFILE VAMPI, TOM BARELY LISTENING TO HER STORY.

④ - C.U. SUDDENLY SPOOKY LOOKING VAMPI, LOOKING BACK OVER HER SHOULDER AT TOM.

Notes:

① FLASHBACK TO THE MARS-LIKE LANDSCAPE OF HELL. LILITH, OBVIOUSLY PREGNANT, WALKS ACROSS PANEL IN REGAL DRESS - HER LONG TRAIN IS HELD ALOFT BY BOWING, SCUTTLING MIDWIVES - THEY LOOK LIKE SOME KIND OF MUMMIFIED NURSES. TONS OF VARIOUS DEMONS STAND AT ATTENTION IN B.G.

② - C.U. LILITH SCREAMING.

③ - PULL BACK, WE SEE HER SPLAYED ON A STONE ALTAR.

④ - PULL BACK, NOW WE SEE HER MIDWIVES DEAD AROUND HER. HER TRAIN STRETCHES OUT BENEATH HER. WE SEE NO NAUGHTY BITS.

⑤ - SILHOUETTE OF BABY VAMPI BEING RAISED BY LILITH IN F.G. - IN B.G. THE HORDES OF DEMONS LOOK AFRAID.

Notes:

① ③ ONE CONTINUOUS SCENE. IN PANEL 1 WE SEE SOME EVIL, SICKLY LOOKING DUDES, IN PANEL 2 WE SEE SOME DEMONIC LOOKING MEN, IN PANEL 3 WE SEE A MONSTROUS DEMON. TRANSFORMATION!

④ - COOL SHOT. SEXY, ACTIONY SHOT OF VAMPI KICKING ALL SORTS OF VAMPIRE/MONSTER ASS - CHOOSE YOUR OWN SHOT!

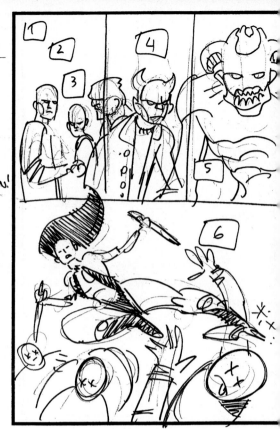

Notes:

① - BACK TO THE PARLOR, VAMPI IS ABOUT TO DROP A BOMB ON HIM, BUT SHE LOOKS ALMOST DREAMY & RELAXED. HE'S FEVERED.

② - FULL SHOT OF VAMPI'S BACK. THERE'S A RAW TATTO OF AN ORNATE, GOTHIC, TRIBAL, WHATEVER FRAME. NOTHING IN IT YET.

③ - FLASHBACK - A WOMAN IS SUSPENDED FROM HOOKS & CHAINS IN F6., BELOW A SHOCKED VAMPIRELLA LOOKS UP AT HER. THE VICTIM IS IN DEEP SHADOW OR SILHOUETTE.

④ - SILHOUETTE OF VAMPI OPENING MOUTH TO RECEIVE A DROP OF BLOOD FALLING FROM VICTIM'S CHIN.

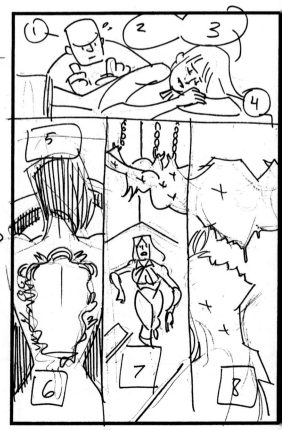

Title: <u>Vampirella- INK</u> **Issue:** <u>Halloween Special</u> **Page:** 11

Notes:

1. — C.U. TOM TATTOOING VAMPI'S BACK. HE'S BARELY LISTENING TO HER TALE.

2. — TECHNICAL TIME! X.C.U. OF TOM'S RIGHT HAND HOLDING THE TATTOO NEEDLE OVER VAMPI'S SKIN - THERE ARE TWO PINHOLES WHERE THE NEEDLE HAS JUST PUNCTURED THE SKIN IN A SEMI-CIRCLE. TINY DROPLETS OF BLOOD WELL FROM THE HOLES. WE CAN SEE THE ELABORATE FRAME ALREADY ON HER BACK.

3. — REPEAT ②, BUT TOM'S HAND (LEFT) SWEEPS OVER THE TAT WITH A BIG GAUZE PAD, SOAKING UP THE BLOOD.

4. PROFILE VAMPI RESTING HEAD ON ARMS.

5. REPEAT ④, BUT SHE'S LOOKING BACK AT US.

6. — C.U. VAMPI'S BACK, TOM IS USING BOTH HANDS TO MOP BLOOD

7. — EVIL VAMPI IN F.G. TOM IN B.G. IS WIPING AWAY WITH BLOOD SOAKED PADS.

Title: <u>Vampirella- INK</u> **Issue:** <u>Halloween Special</u> **Page:** 12

Notes:

1. — C.U. ON TOM WIPING BLOOD AWAY.

2. — SAME, THE BLOOD WELLS UP.

3. — SAME, THE DROPLETS START TO MOVE, LEAVING A TRAIL OF BLOOD, FORMING AN IMAGE.

4. — C.U. OF TOM'S WIFE RENDERED IN BLOOD. WE STILL SEE THE FRAMING TATTOO.

Title: **Vampirella- INK**   Issue: **Halloween Special**   Page: **13**

Notes:

(1) - TOM FALLS BACK FROM VAMPI IN TOTAL FREAK OUT.

(2) - TINY TOM IN B.G. IN F.G. THERE APPEARS TO BE MULTIPLE VERSIONS OF TOM'S SUSPENDED WIFE (IN SILHOUETTE) HANGING FROM CHAINS & HOOKS. GO NUTS.

(3) - NICE SHOT OF VAMPI SITTING UP ON THE TATTOO BED. HER BLOOD TATTOO CLEARLY VISIBLE. SHE'S MERCILESS NOW

(4) - PANICKED TOM STUMBLES BACK INTO THE SUSPENSION CHAINS & HOOKS HE HAS ON DISPLAY.

(5) - C.U. IMPLACABLE VAMPI.

(6) - REPEAT (4), BUT NOW TOM IS DEFIANT, HE'S BRANDISHING ONE OF THE CHAINED HOOKS LIKE A WEAPON.

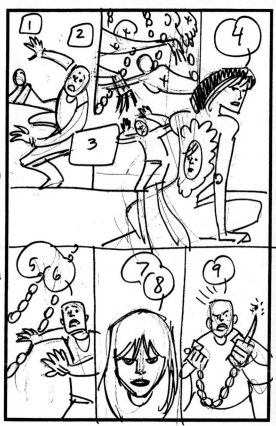

Title: **Vampirella- INK**   Issue: **Halloween Special**   Page: **14**

Notes:

(1) - VAMPI IN ON HIM INSTANTLY - SHE'S YANKED THE HOOK & CHAIN FROM TOM. TOM'S FLAILING ARMS OBSCURE VAMPI'S BOOBS.

(2) - C.U. VAMPI FLASHING HER FANGS, MAYBE TOM'S HEAD IN F.G.

(3) - LONGSHOT. TOM RUNS INTO F.G., SHADOWY VAMPI HOLDS THE HOOK & CHAIN IN B.G.

(4) ... THEN THROWS IT INTO F.G. LIKE A HARPOON.

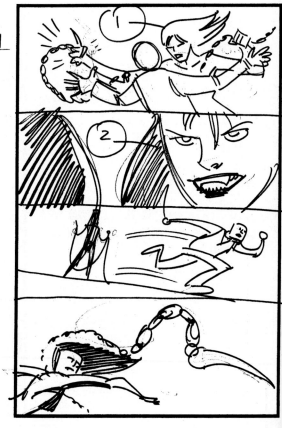

Notes:

(1) - TOM IS LIKE A MARIONETTE TRUSSED UP ON CHAINS (SILHOUETTE) ABOVE VAMPI AS SHE DRESSES.

(2) - C.U. THE BLOODIED, DYING TOM.

(3) - MONEY SHOT OF VAMPI LOOKING BACK AT HIM, HAIR SWINGING TO ONE SIDE TO REVEAL A BACK PURE AS WHEN SHE CAME IN.

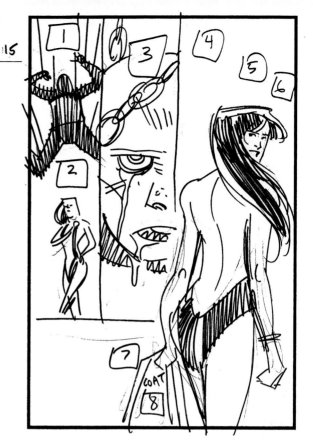

Notes:

(1) - C.U. TOM'S BACK. THERE'S A TATTO OF VAMPI SIMILAR TO THE LAST PANEL LAST PAGE. IN EX. FIG. WE SEE THE NEEDLE-LIKE STINGER OF A SCORPION TAIL, DRIPPING SOME DARK POISON.

(2) - REVERSE SHOT, WE SEE TWO DEMONS. ONE DESIGNED AS YOU WISH, THE SECOND HAS A SCORPION TAIL APPENDAGE GROWING FROM THE BASE OF HIS SKULL, OR BACK OR SOMETHING. HE'S THE TATTOOER.

(3) - C.U. CRYING, SWEATING TOM PLEADING WITH THE DEMONS BEHIND HIM.

(4) - PULL BACK FOR A DOWNSHOT. TOM IS SUSPENDED ON HOOKS OVER A RIVER OF LAVA. THE TWO DEMONS STAND ON A LEDGE NEARBY. HELL.

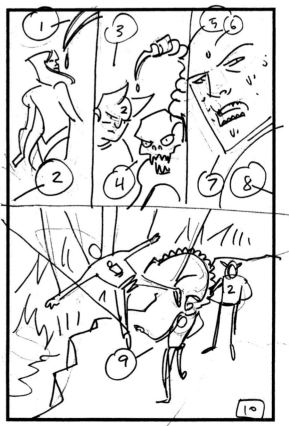

PAGE 1

PANEL 1
A business district in Washington, D.C., we should be able to see some of the DC architecture in the distant background. It's nighttime, and the city's lights are lit.

CAPTION: And so... we accomplish.

CAPTION: We succeed.

PANEL 2
Push in on a building; it's the warehouse from the end of the previous issue.

CAPTION: We set out to do things, and sometimes... even without meaning to...

PANEL 3
The building starts to glow, an explosion brewing inside.

CAPTION: We succeed.

PANEL 4
EXPLOSION!

CAPTION: Even though we meant to fail.

PAGE 2-3

PANEL 1
HUGE PANEL ACROSS THE TOP HALF OF BOTH PAGES - It's the apocalypse. From that mushroom cloud, all of Washington, D.C. is being showered with fire.

CAPTION: The journey of our lives is all that we have... all that we can stand by.

CHAOS (O.P.): And so, by the hand of his greatest enemy, CHAOS was set free.

CHAOS (O.P.): And through the body of his enemy's true love, CHAOS shall rule the Earth.

PANEL 2 (Bottom Left Corner of Page 2)
CHAOS, the emblem burning on the chest that was once Adam Van Helsing, the CHAOS aura blooming from him, his tongue licking at his lips. He's laughing, as the BRQ holds on to him lustfully.

CAPTION: My journey has led me here. To this day. To face the greatest evil this world has ever known.

CHAOS: I don't suppose the irony is lost on you, Vampirella.

PANEL 3
Vampirella is beaten and bruised, pushing herself up from the dust and rubble. She's ready for a fight though.

CAPTION: If that's my destiny, so be it.

VAMPIRELLA: This ends now, Chaos.

PANEL 4
Chaos rises up, the aura pulls a swirl of debris around him, as though it's 'filling itself in' and becoming solid.

CAPTION: I just wish I wasn't scared to death.

CHAOS: I couldn't agree more.

PANEL 5
Chaos raises his now giant fist and SMASHES VAMPIRELLA!

TITLE BOX: VENGEANCE OF VAMPIRELLA, Part 3 of 4
Written by Joshua Hale Fialkov
Art by Stephen Segovia
Colors by Jay David Ramos
Letters by Ed Dukeshire

PAGE 4

PANEL 1
Vampi is left, crushed into the street battered and broken, as CHAOS motions to the Queen.

CHAOS: Come, my Queen... let's have some fun.

PANEL 2
The Queen is giddy as a schoolgirl.

BRQ: Of course, my Lord.

PANEL 3
She spits on Vampirella as she passes by.

BRQ: Take that you blood-sucking bitch.

PANEL 4
Vampi's arm juts out, and grabs the Queen's leg.

PANEL 5
The Queen is on the ground as Vampi rises up; she's like a wild animal, the look of a hungry predator on her face.

VAMPIRELLA: Blood sucking is right.

PAGE 5

PANEL 1
Chaos rises up in the middle of the city, the Washington Monument hanging like a broken twig in the background. Still the debris swirls, making him ever larger and more threatening.

CHAOS: I call on you, my armies of darkness, my hounds of hell, my cursed and broken masses... COME FORTH!

PANEL 2
From Chaos a wave of energy pours forth, through all of the civilians, it's as though they're being electrocuted.

CHAOS: Yes... my victory... OUR victory, my love... where...

VAMPIRELLA (O.P.): OVER HERE, CHAOS.

PANEL 3
Vampirella holds the nearly dead corpse of the Blood Red Queen, the blood dripping from her neck matching the blood on Vampi's face.

VAMPIRELLA: You let them go... now. Or she dies.

PANEL 4
CHAOS smiles as he releases the people.

CHAOS: As you wish.

PANEL 5
But the people are not right... they're transforming before Vampi's horrified eyes into hideous monsters and demons. Twisted soulless monsters with barely a touch of humanity left in them.

PAGE 6 and 7

PANEL 1
Top 2/3rds of the two pages, we see the army of Hell piling on Vampirella. The Blood Red Queen cackles, still in Vampi's hand.

CAPTION: I know I'm beginning to sound like a broken record here, but this is all my fault.

CAPTION: Adam's going to give me hell when I get him back.

CAPTION: Notice, I said 'when' and not 'if.'

CAPTION: That's the power of positive thinking.

BRQ: NOW, FINALLY, YOU DIE!

PANEL 2 - 10
Small, Square Panels lining the bottom of the page, each filled with extreme close-ups of Vampi.

First she slashes the BRQ down

The BRQ's Energy disperses, her body killed.

Vampi tries to dispense with the attacking monsters... but she can't use deadly force... they're still people.

In the final two panels one of them grabs Vampi and bites down on her. She's forced to snap its neck.

If you can do more panels, or lay it out differently, feel free.

BRQ: HAHAHAHAHAHAHAHAHAHAHAH!

CAPTION: I can't kill them... they're still people.

CAPTION: And CHAOS knows that.

CAPTION: I can't do this...

CAPTION: I have to do this.

PAGE 8

PANEL 1
Vampi holds the dead Monster who's slowly transforming back into a human.

VAMPI: Is that what you want Chaos? You want to see me kill? You want to see me destroy these innocents?

VAMPI: FINE.

PANEL 2
Vampi's grabbed another of the hellspawn. She holds him with a death grip.

VAMPI: They're all cursed anyways, right? Every one of them a monster on the inside.

VAMPI: RIGHT?

PANEL 3
CHAOS smiles. He's ruined her...

CHAOS: Something like that... yes.

PANEL 4
Vampirella tosses the creature away, alive, and unscathed.

VAMPI: I'm done playing your games, Chaos.

PANEL 5
Chaos watches, his hands on his hips, the massive junk filled aura turning him into a towering monster, and I'm talking Godzilla size... at his feet, flocking towards Vampi are literally thousands of transformed humans flooding towards her.

CHAOS: I don't think so, my dear.

PAGE 9

PANEL 1
As the horde is pouring at Vampi, Chaos grabs a nearby building and tears it up...

VAMPIRELLA: Don't you get it?

VAMPIRELLA: You can throw ANYTHING at me.

PANEL 2
Vampi launches herself over the horde.

VAMPIRELLA: And until you're back in hell, and I have my Adam back...

PANEL 3
She's crowd surfing, jumping from creature to creature as Chaos wields the building like a gigantic baseball bat.

JOSHUA HALE FIALKOV: On Pages 2 and 3, Stephen manages the near impossible by merging something with massive scope and scale, with the intimate moment of Vampirella's apparent defeat. Seeing CHAOS in all of his twisted glory becomes such a huge moment, and yet, his "acting" is so strong that it becomes a very grounded human moment for every one involved.

VAMPIRELLA: I will not stop.

VAMPIRELLA: I will not surrender.

PANEL 5
Vampi pushes herself off, launching to attack CHAOS who...

PAGE 10

Panel 1
FULL PAGE SPLASH
CHAOS bats Vampirella with the building like she's nothing but a slow ball pitch... it's as though she's a fly, tiny before the mighty rubble body of CHAOS.

JOSHUA HALE FIALKOV: On Page 14, towards the end when Pendragon returns, he takes a character that's been used almost exclusively for comic relief throughout the run of the book, and really drives home that he's not one to be trifled with. There's a raw level of emotion that just bleeds through all of Stephen's pencils that make the world feel extra real, even when what's happening is far from possible.

PAGE 11

PANEL 1
Vampi is just plain **CREAMED.** She's blood soaked, and bruised... lying prone in a pile of rubble.

CHAOS (O.P.): You could've had the world, Vampirella...

CHAOS (O.P.): Together we could've ruled this dimension...

PANEL 2
Vampi starts pushing herself up... but it's tough going.

CHAOS (O.P.): But... oh no... you wouldn't be the Bride of Chaos.

PANEL 3
The Blood Red Queen is looking down at Vampi.

BRQ: You don't need this... thing... anyways, my love.

BRQ: She's nothing.

PANEL 4
Vampirella struggles pushing herself up to her knees, trying to ready herself to fight.

BRQ: Look at her! Look how cute!

BRQ: She thinks she can still win...

PANEL 5
Close on Vampi... anger in her eyes.

BRQ: Look around you, you fool.

BRQ: We already won.

PAGE 12

PANEL 1
We pull back... Earth already looks like Hell. The sky is burning red, the buildings are crumbling, and the Demon/People are running amok.

CHAOS: And so easy... look at them, Vampirella... the ones you want to save...

CHAOS: Not twenty minutes and they're already devolving...

PANEL 2
Push in on two of the Demon/People fighting...

CHAOS: They're nothing but mindless, soulless cattle.

CHAOS: Devoid of value.

PANEL 3
One of the monsters rips out the throat of the other, who starts becoming human again...

CHAOS: And for these beasts you risk YOUR life.

CHAOS: The life of the one you love.

PANEL 4
In the midst of CHAOS's body, Adam's body still sits... it looks like he's sleeping.

CHAOS: Your beloved Adam can't contain my life force for much longer, Vampirella. Soon, he'll become just another piece of me.

PANEL 5
XCU on Vampi's face, she looks ready to cry...

VAMPI: Adam... I'm coming...

PAGE 13

PANEL 1-3
(Should be one wide panel, split into three smaller panels, with Vampi moving through them)

Wide, cinematic motion shots, Vampi running and leaping from her perch of rubble up towards CHAOS's chest, where Adam's body sits.

PANEL 4
One of CHAOS's giant rubble hands grabs Vampi out of the air.

PANEL 5
Vampi squirms trying to escape, straining with all of her might.

CHAOS: Is that it? Is that ALL you have? You're going to run and jump and hit and slash at ME?

PANEL 6
The CHAOS 'construct' so to speak, towering over Vampi... he's in full on Mad God mode now.

CHAOS: I AM GOD.

CHAOS: And you... are nothing.

PAGE 14

PANEL 1
CHAOS gets blasted by a HUGE plume of magical energy, dropping Vampi in the process.

PANEL 2
We see the origin of that bolt of magic. Pendragon.

PENDRAGON: Get the hell away from my assistant.

PANEL 3
Chaos laughs.

CHAOS: YOU?!? Mordecai Pendragon... drunk and deviant... the man who would sell his own soul for a glass of bourbon.

CHAOS: Are you so inebriated that you think you're a REAL magician.

PANEL 4
Pendragon stands on a crest facing CHAOS.

PENDRAGON: No, you ancient fool... I know I'm barely a match for a flea, let alone you.

PANEL 5
Pendragon cracks a mischievous smile.

PENDRAGON: That's why I bought some friends along.

PAGE 15

PANEL 1
From around Pendragon come magicians of all kinds. Their hands all glow with the energy that Pen used to save the civilians earlier.

PENDRAGON: Y'see, Chaos... I did a lot of touring.

PENDRAGON: And met a LOT of other magicians.

PANEL 2
Two particularly menacing looking warlocks step forward.

PENDRAGON: And, well, as my lovely assistant would say...

PENDRAGON: I'm nothing if not charming.

PANEL 3
The magicians have formed a circle around Pendragon and CHAOS.

PENDRAGON: And over the past god knows how many years, you and your cult have pissed off the wrong bunch of magic users.

PANEL 4
Chaos readies himself for battle.

CHAOS: So it shall be.

CHAOS: Now, we fight.

PANEL 5
Pendragon gives a knowing wink.

PENDRAGON: You HONESTLY think I would fight you? After all this time?

PENDRAGON: There's only one fight for you, big guy.

PANEL 6
High, wide shot, the magician's energy channels into a spot in the rubble.

PAGE 16

PANEL 1
Small Thin Wide panel - A hand pulls out of the rubble.

PANEL 2
Small Thin Wide Panel - Another hand starts to pull the rest of her out of the rubble. The hands are glowing with the Good Magical energy.

PANEL 3
REST OF PAGE
Vampirella, a battle Aura formed around her, and she looks totally f***g juiced up. It's like she has the power of all 300 of the wussy Spartan boys powering her.**

VAMPIRELLA: Now.

VAMPIRELLA: Can we just end this already?

TO BE CONCLUDED!

JOSHUA HALE FIALKOV:
It's pretty rare, as a writer, to find an artist like Stephen. He manages to cross so many lines with his work. Most guys are either architecture guys, or character guys, or they do great designs but are inexpressive, or vice versa. Stephen can literally do it all. As you've seen throughout the rest of the book, there's just nothing you can throw at him that he can't execute the hell out of.

It's been an honor and a great learning experience for me to work with Stephen. I can only hope it's not the last time we collaborate.

VENGEANCE OF VAMPIRELLA

RETURN OF THE BLOOD RED QUEEN

Executive Publisher Jonathan Rheingold
Director-Publishing & Editorial Bon Alimagno
Creative Director Rommel Alama
Webmaster Lisa Case
Publishing Assistant Chris Caniano

HARRIS PUBLICATIONS
President & Publisher Stanley Harris
Chief Financial Officer Warren Sherman
Production Director Dennis M. Wheeler
Director of Pre-Press Phil Dhom

Editorial Offices
1115 Broadway, New York, NY 10010
Ph: 212-807-7100 • Fax: 212-620-7787
E-mail: comics@harris-pub.com
vampirella.com